The Secret of Pig Island

Ocean Education Publishing
712 Pelican Way
North Palm Beach, Florida 33408

"Ocean Education Publishing strives to teach and inspire us all to value and protect our oceans."

Library of Congress Cataloging — in Publication data.
ISBN 978-0-615-40721-0
Printed in China by Everbest through Four Colour Print Group

CPSIA Tracking Label Information
Production Location: Printed by Everbest Printing Co. Ltd., Nansha, China
Production Date: 10/12/2010
Job/Batch #: 97639

The Secret of Pig Island

Jennifer R. Nolan

Photography by James R. Abernethy

Edited by Tory Dietel Hopps
Graphic design by Lazaro Ruda

Ocean Education Publishing, North Palm Beach

This book is dedicated to all those individuals who help protect our environment and to all those who will follow in their footsteps.

Inspiration for The Secret of Pig Island

In the summer of 2007, Jennifer Nolan and Tory Dietel Hopps traveled to the tropical blue waters of the Bahamas for a weeklong, wild dolphin encounter that was organized by *BlueVoice.org*, an environmental organization founded by Hardy Jones and Ted Danson. They lived aboard the Shear Water, captained by Jim Abernethy, an award-winning underwater photographer and dedicated conservationist. This unique opportunity to spend some sacred time at sea, immersed in the playful world of the wild dolphins and other beautiful marine life, inspired these two authors to help spread the word about caring for our beautiful paradise, Earth.

During this adventure, Abernethy was asked to share some of his underwater images with his guests. What Jennifer and Tory soon discovered in his files were hundreds of captivating images that ranged from friendly, spotted dolphins to close ups of magnificent tiger sharks. To their surprise, amidst his collection were photos of wild pigs living along the tropical beaches of the Bahamas. Weeks later, Jennifer created Plato and his buddies that have a message to share with us all: *Our planet is our paradise. Let's all care for Mother Earth.*

I heard there is an island in the tropical blue sea
where wild pigs are roaming; I wondered could it be?
I heard they have a secret they really wish to share.
But how to find this island? More important, do I dare?

Will I really care about this messy gang of pigs?

Who would want to hang around their stinky island digs.

They spend all day tossing dirt, then trash the place they sleep.

Yet off I go to meet these pigs—a secret they do keep!

I hurried to the dock and hopped into my boat.

Untied all the knotted ropes, then off I went afloat.

Minutes turned to hours as I cruised across the sea.

So curious to find what fate awaited me.

Eventually before my eyes stood emerald shades of green:

An island full of palm trees. Perhaps it was a dream.

From the bow I shouted, "I see the pigs from here!"
Spotted, hairy creatures with big ears were drawing near.
Unsure if they'd be my friends, I lifted up my oar.
How my heart was racing as they gathered on the shore.

A pig swam out to greet me through waves of turquoise blue.

He said, "Welcome, I am Plato. It's a pleasure meeting you."

I shook his tiny hoof; then he said, "Let's take a swim."

"If pigs can do it, you can too!" he squealed…so I dove in!

Off he swam, four legs and tail, moving right along.

Who'd have guessed a little pig in water was so strong.

"You've landed on Pig Island; a treasure you will find.

Glad you're here, we've much to share with you and humankind."

He rolled around, then jumped back up, and raised his sandy snout.

"Time to search for clues," he said, "I'll help you scout them out!"

"Is there shiny gold," I asked, "a treasure hid somewhere?

I must admit I wonder—will I be a millionaire?"

It was then he motioned me to come in really close.

I leaned right in to catch each word from my island host.

"Our secret," Plato whispered, "it's more valuable than gold.

Hog heaven is a place where there's a lesson to behold."

"Come, let's go," a piglet called, as Plato led the way.

We skedaddled down the beach, amidst the ocean spray.

I searched and searched for any sign, I wanted so to learn.

Yet in the sun, and in the shade, no hint at any turn.

Plato stood in front of me, a twinkle in his eye.

"Perhaps it's what you do not see that comes as a surprise.

Here's a hint: Look over there beside the Banyan trees.

See any mess, unsightly trash, big piles of debris?

You know a feisty herd of pigs can make a stinky smell.

But how we love to care about the island where we dwell.

We love to root, dig some holes, wag our curly tails,

but any swine who leaves a mess is heading off to jail.

The reason that we sent for you is right beneath your feet.

It's all about our precious Earth and how to keep it neat!

It's come to our attention, people can be piggy too.

The time is now for everyone to *join the clean-up crew*.

You see it's very simple; this island is our home.

People have one planet. There's nowhere else to roam.

Mother Earth is asking us to care for her with pride.

From our tiny island, would you spread our message wide?

You see we're pigs...but squeaky clean. That's our solemn vow.

If pigs can do it, you can too! The time to start is now."

"Plato, you have much to say for such a puny pig.

It's clear to me the change we need is simple but it's big!

Not a minute should I waste to make this Earth like new.

Off I go to spread the word: *Change begins with you!*"

It was then those silly swine wiggled, squiggled, and rolled.

Soon one yelled, "Hooray! Hooray! You finally found our gold!"

"Right before my eyes," I said, "I see the secret clear.

People, pigs, anyone, protect what they hold dear."

With new found friends all around, how they touched my heart.

We danced and sang, till like the sun, the time came to depart.

Swimming to my anchored boat, Plato splashed away.

How I wished to find the words to thank him for this day.

Reaching out to give a hug, I spoke into his ear.

"I promise you I'm heading home to gather volunteers."

He turned to me and with a wink, said, "Thanks for taking action.

The planet is our paradise. It's the main attraction!"

Then off he jumped, four legs and tail, into the water blue.

Singing for us all to hear, "Pigs can do it, you can too!"

Thanks for joining the clean-up crew. Let's all dive in!

1. Reduce your environmental footprint: REDUCE, REUSE, REYCYLE.
2. Encourage family and friends to vote for elected officials who pledge to protect the environment.
3. Join advocacy groups and organizations that help to protect our environment. Become a member and a volunteer.
4. Sign petitions that strive to promote living in harmony with Mother Earth.
5. Consider the well-being of the planet in all your actions. Every effort makes a difference!

Check it out! Here are some organizations that are making a real difference.

Environmental Defense Fund: www.edf.org

Greenpeace: www.greenpeace.org

Natural Resource Defense Council: www.nrdc.org

Oceana: www.oceana.org

Sierra Club: www.sierraclub.org

World Wildlife Fund: www.worldwildlife.org

Through the eyes of the photographers~

When Eric and I found ourselves literally in "hog heaven," amidst this extraordinary example of an island paradise, little did we know the images would later inspire the creation of a children's book, complete with a message of global conservation. As nature photographers, we travel to some of the world's best, kept secrets in pursuit of capturing nature's magnificence. Knowing that those images might encourage others to help protect the very environment so dear to our hearts is what keeps us behind the lens, in search of the next best shot to share with all of you. Enjoy.

– Jim Abernethy & Eric Cheng

Acknowledgments

We wish to thank Eric Cheng for his photographic contributions to this book, seen on pages 8, 12, 16, 17, 24, 29, 32 and 40. We are most grateful!

We would also like to express our appreciation to Kelly Bracken (pg. 21) and Don Kehoe (pg. 36 & 40) for their images.

To family and friends, we extend our deepest appreciation for all the support during the creation of this book. To graphic designer, Lazaro Ruda, much gratitude is owed for his time and expertise.

A special "thanks" goes out to Weston Nolan for his time spent in multiple photo shoots for this project. Plato thanks you all too!

Jennifer R. Nolan is a freelance writer and currently collaborates with photographer Jim Abernethy on a series of marine life books about threatened species. Jennifer serves as president of RockHopp LLC, a small company she started with Tory Dietel Hopps, that develops innovative ideas for the marketplace with a focus on education, children and the environment. They created a multi-award winning book, *Spintastik*, that was released in 2005. She has served on multiple nonprofit boards and is a passionate environmentalist. Jennifer lives in Maine with her husband and four sons.

Tory Dietel Hopps is a philanthropic advisor, helping private clients realize the change they hope to see in the world through their charitable endeavors. She has enjoyed a lifelong involvement with the nonprofit sector and is particularly dedicated to children and the environment. In 2003, Tory teamed up with Jennifer Nolan to form RockHopp Partners, LLC. Tory lives in Maine with her husband and two children.

Jim Abernethy is an award-winning underwater photographer and specializes in shark encounters without a cage. His marine life images are often featured in top photography magazines such as WetPixel and Nature's Best Photography. His first book, *Sharks Up Close*, was released in 2009. He is the owner/operator of Scuba Adventures, a dive business that brings nature lovers and photographers up close to a wide range of species, from sharks to dolphins, and on occasion, even pigs. While running expeditions, his business has hosted many of the world's top nature filmmakers and magazines such as: IMAX, National Geographic, BBC Wildlife and Discovery Channel. Abernethy lives at sea but calls Palm Beach, Florida his home.

You are invited to visit his website at www.scuba-adventures.com

Eric Cheng is an award-winning underwater photographer known for his passion as an educator. His photography has been represented in numerous magazines and books worldwide, and his underwater imagery has been seen at venues like the Smithsonian's Natural History Museum.

Eric is the editor and publisher of Wetpixel.com, the premiere online community for underwater photographers. In all of his endeavors, Eric strives to provide a forum for photographers to share their work and discuss ocean-related issues, and in turn, educate viewers about the beauty and fragility of the marine ecosystem.

Eric's underwater images can be found on his personal website: http://echeng.com